To all those in Karigiri who inspired the book.

Huge thanks to all the people who made Bela possible.

With special thanks to Ben Drayton, Trevor Leigh, Anne Muir, Alex Schlich and family.

Bela
First Edition

For ordering and more information visit:
The Leprosy Mission Scotland www.tlmscotland.co.uk

First Published by Mia Hadrill
Text copyright © 2013 Mia Hadrill
Illustrations copyright © 2013 Jessica Kettle

Hardback: ISBN 978-0-9926286-0-4
Paperback: ISBN 978-0-9926286-1-1

Book design by Rosie Smith www.rosiesmithdesign.co.uk

Bela

Teacher

Mani

Sita

Mama

Grandma

Local Healer

Raju

Anita

Baby Brother

Doctor

Papa

Friends

"Wait for me," called Sita, as Bela raced ahead.

There was **Anita**, selling pails of creamy **buffalo milk**.

There was **Mani**, who served Papa's favourite piping hot cups of **chai tea**

RAJU'S SWEETS

...and there was Raju's splendid sweet cart...

...where Bela always got a big piece for her rupees!

"Look what I can do," grinned Bela.

Mama noticed some nasty looking **blisters** on **Bela's foot** and tutted.

"That's enough silliness," said Mama, "Come inside and help me cook."

When Bela tried to flip her dosa pancake, she **didn't feel** the hot pan burn her hand.

"Go and sweep instead," called Mama. But Bela's arm would **not do** what it was told.

Grandma inspected the white patches on Bela's arm. "Insect bites," she said.

Grandma made a special medicine, but it did not work.
Bela's condition just got worse and worse.

"Let's try the local healer?"
suggested Mama.

"It's leprosy!"
whispered the village.

"Leprosy means you **can't feel pain**,
but don't worry Bela.
We'll soon have you **better**."

Bela took her **medicine**...

...massaged her clean **hands** and **feet**

...and did her **exercises**.

Bela could **not wait** to see all her **friends**...

but her friends still **didn't want** to play.

But **something** was happening...

Bela hid behind a wall to watch the **excitement**.

People from the hospital came to the village, and **performed** a **play** all about leprosy.

"Bela!" exclaimed her brother

Sita placed a marigold garland round Bela's neck, gave her an extra big hug...

and giggled "last one to the tree is a mouldy mango!"

Leprosy Explained

What is leprosy?

Leprosy, also called Hansen's disease, or HD, is caused by a germ called *Mycobacterium leprae*. Disease is when you are not healthy.

Where is leprosy found?

Leprosy used to be a problem in the UK and Europe. Now it is found in hot and humid tropical and subtropical areas in the world.

Leprosy is mainly found in places of poverty, which means people with leprosy are often poorer than others around them.

? Did you know that armadillos in America carry leprosy?

How do you catch leprosy?

It is spread from person to person via droplets in coughs and sneezes.

It is very hard to get leprosy, because 95% of people are naturally immune, which means they cannot catch it.

What does it do to the body?

The first sign of leprosy is usually skin patches, which look a different colour. A person with leprosy does not feel anything if the patch is tickled with a feather.

Leprosy can stay in the body for many years without showing any signs. Many people who have leprosy don't find out until years after the germ went inside their body.

Leprosy affects nerves, which carry messages between the brain and body. It mainly affects the colder areas of the body, such as the nose, eyes, throat, hands and feet.

Leprosy can cause blindness, disability (not being able to do things) and disfigurement (changing the way the body looks). It can stop people feeling pain in affected areas on their skin.

? Did you know that pain is important? Without it we do not know if something is too hot or too sharp and we can easily get hurt.

Treatment

Multidrug therapy, or MDT, is a mix of medicines that cure leprosy. The cure was found in the 1980s. Very soon after taking the pills people with leprosy stop passing on the germ. The quicker a person takes medicine the better it is to stop them having problems in the future.

Misconceptions and myths

Misconception means believing something that is untrue. Myths are unproved, invented ideas. Here are some common myths and misconceptions about leprosy and all are false:

- Leprosy causes body parts to fall off,
- Leprosy is easy to catch,
- You catch leprosy from touching someone who has it,
- Everyone with leprosy looks different from those who do not have it,
- People with leprosy should not be allowed to be around other people.

Social Issues

Prejudice is when someone believes something, and makes up their mind about a person because of that belief, without knowing the person or the truth. Leprosy patients are often avoided by others because of misconceptions. It hurts their feelings a lot.

? How would you feel if someone made up their mind about you without knowing anything about you?

Share What You Know

Explaining to people about leprosy helps them to understand that leprosy is not a big deal. No one should be treated badly because they are different from you or others. That is called 'discrimination' and is very unfair and hurtful.

Now that you know about leprosy you can tell other people the truth!

Snakes & Ladders

Play snakes and ladders with Bela.

In some parts of India it is mistakenly believed that snakes, especially those with two heads, are the cause of leprosy.

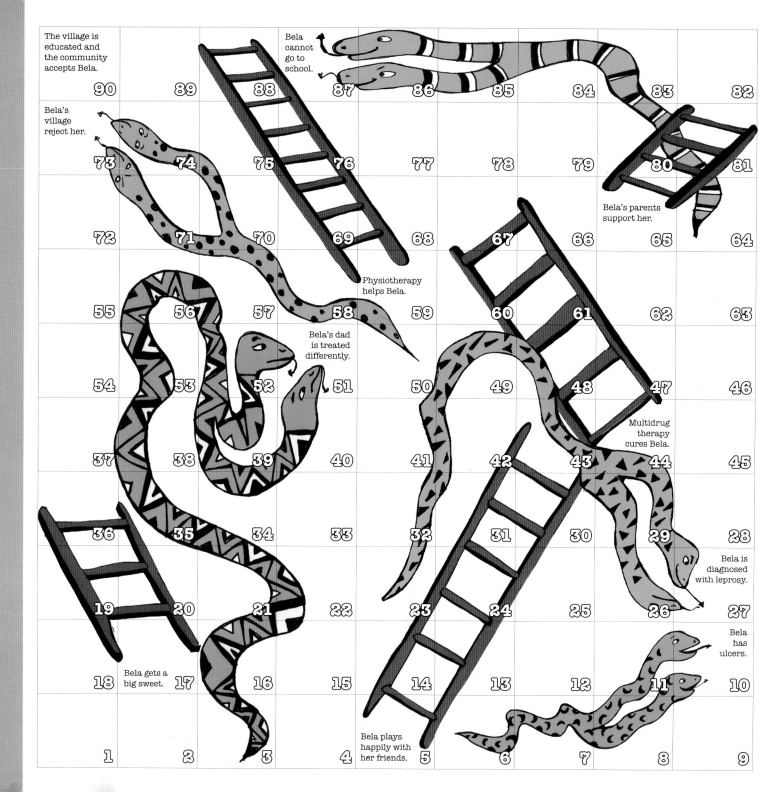